Piano Exam Pieces

ABRSM Initial Grade

Selected from the 2021 & 2022 syllabus

Name

Date o

D0256140

Contents

Editor for ABRSM: Richard Jones
Footnotes: Sally Cathcart and Richard Jones

Other pieces for Initial Grade

LIST A

4 **Gurlitt** Dance (No. 2 from *Das Kleines Konzert*, Op. 227). *Music Pathways: Repertoire, Level 3A* (Carl Fischer)

5 **Humbert** The Black Forest Doll: No. 3 from *Allerlei Spielzeug* (Schott)

6 **Kabalevsky** A Little Scherzo: No. 6 from *24 Easy Pieces*, Op. 39 (Boosey & Hawkes)

7 **A. Reinagle** Allegretto: No. 9 from *24 Short and Easy Pieces*, Op. 1 (Schott) or *Pianissimo: Piano Piccolo* (Schott)

8 **Bertram Schattel** Racing Against Each Other (*primo part*): No. 12 from *For Rosalie and Finn* (pp. 23-24) (Breitkopf & Härtel) DUET

9 **Trad. Irish** John Ryan's Polka, arr. Blackwell. *Piano Star 2* (ABRSM)

10 **Elsie Wells** Donkey Ride (from *Sea Pictures, Set 1*) (*primo part*). *Duets with a Difference: Piano Time Duets, Book 1* (OUP) DUET

LIST B

4 **June Armstrong** Butterfly (*primo part*). *Piano Star Duets* (ABRSM) DUET

5 **Pauline Hall** The Secret Garden (*pedalling optional*). *Piano Time Pieces 1* (OUP)

6 **Alison Mathews** Sailing Under a Moonlit Sky (*una corda optional*). *Mosaic, Vol. 1* (Editions Musica Ferrum)

7 **Christopher Norton** Enchanted Castle (*primo part*): No. 6 from *The Microjazz Duets Collection 1* (Boosey & Hawkes) DUET

8 **Orff** No. 1 (from *Two Pieces*). *From Bartók to Stravinsky* (Schott)

9 **Satie** What the Little Princess Tulip Says (No. 2 from *Menus propos enfantins*). *Satie: Nine Children's Pieces* (ABRSM) or *Pianissimo: Piano Piccolo* (Schott)

10 **Pam Wedgwood** Whirleybird: No. 2 from *Up-Grade! Piano Grades 0-1* (Faber) or *Pam Wedgwood: Piano for Fun* (Faber)

LIST C

4 **Pauline Hall & Paul Drayton** Stegosaurus Stomp: from *Prehistoric Piano Time* (OUP)

5 **Heather Hammond** Action Stations. *Piano Star 2* (ABRSM)

6 **Mark Tanner** Wonkey Donkey. *Piano Star 2* (ABRSM)

7 **Alan Haughton** Treading Carefully. *Piano Time Going Places* (OUP)

8 **Elton John** I Just Can't Wait to Be King (from *The Lion King*), arr. N. & R. Faber (*student part; with repeat*). *Faber Studio Collection: Selections from ShowTime Piano, Level 2A* (Faber Piano Adventures) DUET

9 **Gerald Martin** Boogie No. 1. *The Joy of Boogie and Blues* (Yorktown Music Press)

10 **Jane Sebba** The Grand Waltz (*primo part*). *Piano Magic Duets, Book 1* (Collins Music) DUET

Published in 2020 by ABRSM (Publishing) Ltd, a wholly owned subsidiary of ABRSM, 4 London Wall Place, London EC2Y 5AU, United Kingdom

© 2020 by The Associated Board of the Royal Schools of Music
Distributed worldwide by Oxford University Press

Music origination by Julia Bovee
Cover by Kate Benjamin & Andy Potts, with thanks to Brighton College
Printed in England by Halstan & Co. Ltd, Amersham, Bucks., on materials from sustainable sources.
P14665

A Marching Tune

No. 1 from *Tunetime*

Dorothy Parke
(1904–90)

This crisp and neat tune was written by Dorothy Parke, a composer from Northern Ireland. Imagine soldiers marching along, being kept in step by the rhythmical playing of a band, especially the drums.

© 1976 Dorothy Parke

Reproduced by permission of Goodmusic Publishing Ltd. www.goodmusicpublishing.co.uk

Gavotte in G

from *Terpsichore*

Arranged by Richard Jones

Michael Praetorius
(1571–1621)

poco rit.

A gavotte is a lively dance with two beats in a bar. Although the composer Michael Praetorius was a church organist, he clearly enjoyed dancing as he wrote over 300 dances in a set called *Terpsichore*. In this Gavotte, the contrast of dynamics, slurs and staccato gives it a lovely sparkle.

© 2020 by The Associated Board of the Royal Schools of Music

This old man

 A:3

Arranged by David Blackwell

Trad. English

'This old man' is a traditional English children's nursery rhyme and counting song. The words of the first verse are:

> This old man, he played one,
> He played knick-knack on my thumb,
> Knick-knack paddywhack,
> Give a dog a bone,
> This old man came rolling home.

In this arrangement, the tune is often shared between the two hands.

© 2016 by The Associated Board of the Royal Schools of Music
Reproduced from *Piano Star 2* (ABRSM)

B:1

The Lost Bone

No. 9 from *Little Dog Tales*

Yvonne Adair
(1897–1989)

This is from a set of pieces called *Little Dog Tales* by Yvonne Adair. The hero of the story is a naughty puppy called Boots. Boots has just dropped his bone so that he can chase rabbits. According to the story, when he finds there are no rabbits about he 'comes back and finds his bone gone. He is very depressed.'

In the exam, the small, bracketed notes in bars 4 and 12 are optional.

B:2

Under the Acacia Tree

from *Safari*

June Armstrong
(born 1951)

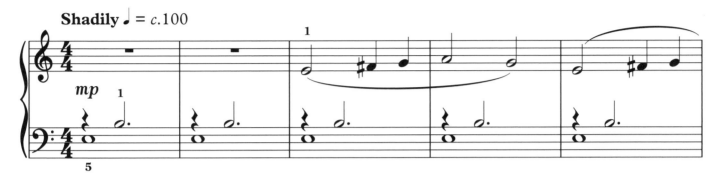

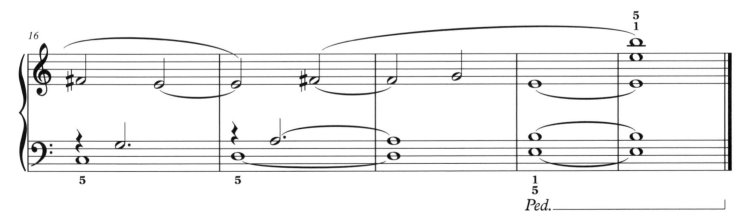

The simple, repeated left-hand rhythm and smooth, stepwise moving melody help to create the calm and peaceful atmosphere of sitting under an acacia tree in Africa. The piece is from *Safari*, a collection of 23 characterful pieces by composer June Armstrong.

Dialogue

from *First Term at the Piano*

Béla Bartók
(1881–1945)

The Hungarian composer Béla Bartók was a fine pianist who wrote a number of collections of pieces for piano students, including *First Term at the Piano*, which this piece comes from. The two hands have a conversation throughout, with the left hand imitating the right hand a bar behind each time. Although the composer's metronome mark is ♩ = 96, students may prefer a quicker tempo, for example ♩ = *c*.108. The dynamics in bars 5, 9, 13 and 15 are editorial suggestions only.

With kind permission of Editio Musica Budapest Zeneműkiadó Ltd

Dodgems

from *Party Time! On Holiday*

C:1

Alan Bullard
(born 1947)

Dodgems are fairground cars that bump into each other, sometimes getting into such a tangle they come to a complete halt. There are big contrasts in dynamics in this piece by British composer Alan Bullard, with lots of drama and a few crashes along the way. It's up to the performer to decide how long it takes to reset the dodgem cars in the pauses.

The indication 'Keeping to the left' is a reference to driving on the left-hand side of the road (as is the case in the United Kingdom), something that isn't required when riding the dodgems! Although the composer's metronome mark is ♩ = 88, students may prefer a slower tempo, for example ♩ = *c*.80.

 C:2

The Elephant Parade

Nikki Iles
(born 1963)

With a heavy feeling ♩ = *c*.80

Imagine a long line of elephants lumbering heavily along. The staccato and tenuto markings, along with the accents, suggest the line might be a little unsteady at times. The composer of this piece, Nikki Iles, is a well-known British jazz pianist and composer.

The Long-Eared Bear

Medvídek Ušáček

No. 1 from *Pohádky na dobrou noc*

Ivana Loudová
(1941–2017)

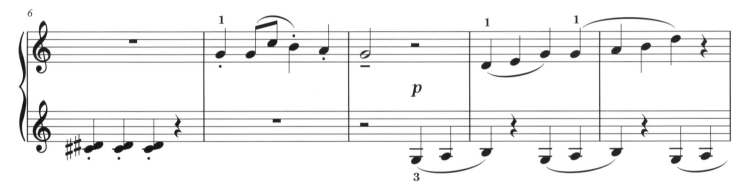

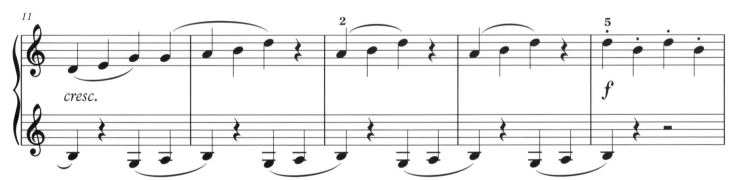

This piece was written by Czech composer Ivana Loudová and is the first of ten small piano pieces with the name *Pohádky na dobrou noc* (Good Night Fairytales). It is perhaps inspired by a bear who became popular on Polish television in the 1970s. The bear's name is Medvídek Ušáček (or Miś Uszatek in the original Polish) and in each episode, just before he goes to bed, he tells a story about the events of his day. This first piece sets the scene for the fairy tales, perhaps with the words 'time for bed' matching the opening notes. The last chord is very quiet – maybe the bear has fallen asleep?